Twelve Steps for Tobacco Users

For People Addicted to Nicotine

REVISED

by Jeanne E.

HAZELDEN

Hazelden
Center City, Minnesota 55012-0176

1-800-328-9000
1-651-213-4590 (Fax)
www.hazelden.org

09 08 07 06   9 8 7 6

About the pamphlet

This pamphlet offers hope and help for those addicted to nicotine who are willing
to try a "new" way of quitting tobacco and staying tobacco-free. It describes how
to use the Twelve Step philosophy to recover from addiction to nicotine. The
author offers guidance and practical tips to start the process of recovery from a
life-threatening obsession.

Editor's note

The Twelve Steps of Nicotine Anonymous are reprinted with permission of
Nicotine Anonymous World Services. Nicotine Anonymous does not endorse
any outside program, and permission to reprint is not an indication that Nicotine
Anonymous has reviewed or approved the contents of this publication.

The brief excerpt from the book *Twelve Steps and Twelve Traditions* of Alcoholics
Anonymous and the Twelve Steps of Nicotine Anonymous (NicA), as adapted by
NicA with permission of Alcoholics Anonymous World Services, Inc. (AAWS), are
reprinted with permission of NicA and AAWS. The Twelve Steps of Alcoholics
Anonymous are reprinted with the permission of AAWS. AAWS's permission
to reprint the foregoing material does not mean that AAWS has reviewed or
approved the contents of this publication, or that AAWS necessarily agrees with
the views expressed herein. Alcoholics Anonymous is a program of recovery from
alcoholism *only*—use or permissible adaptation of AA's Twelve Steps in connection
with programs and activities which are patterned after AA, but which address
other problems, or in any other non-AA context, does not imply otherwise.

Introduction

If you're one of the sixty million cigarette smokers in the United States, you'll want to know one important statistic: cigarettes kill half of those who continue to use them. More than 25 percent of the population in the United States currently smoke, and tobacco use is rising among youth—despite the fact that, a decade ago, the U.S. surgeon general concluded that nicotine is addictive and the third-leading cause of death in this country. If you use tobacco products, you can count yourself among these statistics.

The good news is that, though millions of people use tobacco products, many want to quit. We know that quitting is difficult. Like cocaine, nicotine takes only seconds to reach the brain and stimulates intense craving. Uncomfortable withdrawal symptoms occur within twenty-four hours of abstaining. It's hard to quit and easy to start again. Several attempts may be necessary, but quitting is possible through persistence. Each attempt to quit garners the smoker more information about what helps and what harms efforts to live tobacco-free.

If you're one of those who use tobacco but wish to stop, you'll want to know another important fact: according to the National Institute on Drug Abuse, only 10 percent of those who try to quit without help succeed in doing so; 20 to 25 percent quit by using a single helping resource; and 35 to 40 percent quit and remain abstinent by using a combination of approaches.[1]

You can increase your chances of quitting and staying tobacco-free by using more than one resource. Helpful supports to quitting might include a smoking-cessation program, medication, written materials, and self-help groups.

---

1. National Institute on Drug Abuse, *NIDA Notes: Facts about Nicotine and Tobacco Products* 13, no. 3 (2000).

The Twelve Step program of Alcoholics Anonymous also offers an effective way to understand and accept nicotine addiction and take practical actions to quit.[2] It can be a means to maintain a healthy, balanced lifestyle that leaves little room for addictive behaviors.

The Twelve Step philosophy evolved during the formation of Alcoholics Anonymous and has been used for decades in overcoming alcoholism and other addictions. The Steps can be applied with great success to recovery from addiction to nicotine. This pamphlet will help you honestly face the fact that tobacco use prevents healthy, balanced living and makes day-to-day life unmanageable.

The following pages outline the ways I adapted the Twelve Steps of Alcoholics Anonymous to my nicotine addiction. I found that the parallels between addiction to alcohol and addiction to nicotine are clear—and so are the recovery Steps.

Since the first edition of this pamphlet, the U.S. surgeon general has released several additional reports about the addictive nature of nicotine, its effect on special populations, and its impact on the lives of young people. This updated edition provides current information that will help you better understand the addiction you struggle with and how to begin a life of recovery. I hope you find help and encouragement in these pages.

Facts about Nicotine Addiction

Since 1964, the U.S. surgeon general has released reports that focus on tobacco use and its health consequences for Americans. In a May 1988 report, the surgeon general classified nicotine as addictive.[3] The report called tobacco use "disease producing

---

2. The Twelve Steps of Alcoholics Anonymous are reprinted on page 31.

3. *The Health Consequences of Smoking: Nicotine Addiction, A Report of the Surgeon General* (U.S. Department of Health and Human Services, May 1988).

and life-threatening." Key conclusions of this report include the following:

- Cigarettes and other forms of tobacco are addictive.

- Nicotine is the drug in tobacco that causes addiction.

- The pharmacological and behavioral processes that determine tobacco addiction are similar to those that determine addiction to drugs such as heroin and cocaine.

What does this mean for you? The fact that the nicotine in tobacco is addictive means three things:

- Nicotine creates both a physical and a psychological dependency.

- Nicotine creates a cycle of craving that is only stopped by using more nicotine or by not using it at all.

- Abstaining from nicotine causes withdrawal symptoms.

The 2000 report of the surgeon general states that, though progress has been made in reducing tobacco use since the 1964 report on tobacco was published, approximately one-quarter of adult Americans smoke and the number of young people who smoke has steadily increased.[4] Tobacco use remains the leading cause of death and of preventable illness in the United States. Currently, the best-known way to stop tobacco use and remain abstinent is through combining pharmacological and behavioral therapies.

The Primary Indicators of Drug Dependence

The following signs of drug dependence occur in nicotine dependency as well as in dependency on other drugs:

---

4. *Reducing Tobacco Use: A Report of the Surgeon General* (U.S. Department of Health and Human Services, Centers for Disease Control and Prevention, National Center for Chronic Disease Prevention and Health Promotion, Office on Smoking and Health, 2000).

- *Compulsive use:* drug-seeking and drug-taking behavior is driven by strong, often irresistible urges; it can persist despite a desire and attempts to quit.
- *Mood-altering effects:* the drug affects the brain and moves into the bloodstream.
- *Drug-reinforced behavior:* the drug actively reinforces behavior that leads to taking more of the drug.

These signs are used to further describe drug dependence:

- *Addictive behavior:* repeated patterns of use; continued use despite negative consequences; episodes of quitting and using; and persistent cravings (urges) to use the drug, especially while abstinent from it.

- *Dependence on the drug:* includes diminished responsiveness (that is, increased tolerance) to the drug, resulting in increased intake; physical dependence as indicated by withdrawal symptoms when use ceases; and pleasant effects that are produced by taking the drug.

It may be helpful to study the above dependency characteristics in relation to your own use of nicotine.

It may also help to be aware of these facts specific to nicotine addiction:

- Light and regular cigarettes contain similar amounts of nicotine and toxins, thus "light" brands are as addictive and poisonous as regular brands.

- Switching the nicotine delivery system (cigarette, cigar, chewing tobacco, pipe) as a way to decrease smoking is not effective. It's not the delivery system but the amount of nicotine the delivery system contains that matters. For example, a regular cigarette contains 12 mg to 14 mg of nicotine while a cigar may contain more than 400 mg.

- The various methods of absorbing nicotine—through the mouth, nose, or lungs—yield the same level of nicotine in the blood.

- Daily tobacco users are exposed to the effects of nicotine twenty-four hours a day because, used regularly, nicotine accumulates in the body during the day and persists overnight.

- Users develop tolerance to many of the effects of nicotine, which means higher doses are needed to produce the same stimulation.

- Tobacco users experience withdrawal symptoms within twenty-four hours of stopping use.

- Nicotine is a powerful agent that acts in the brain and throughout the body.

- At high exposure levels, nicotine is a potent and potentially lethal toxin.

- In addition to nicotine, cigarette smoke contains more than four thousand substances, many of which can damage the lungs or cause cancer.

- Secondhand smoke puts others at risk. Nearly 90 percent of nonsmokers in the United States over age four have detectable levels of a chemical marker that indicates exposure to environmental tobacco smoke.[5]

- Long-term tobacco users are exposed to substantial levels of nicotine, affecting many organ systems in the body.

The facts about tobacco use and nicotine addiction present strong parallels to other drug dependencies and equally strong

---

5. *Reducing Tobacco Use: A Report of the Surgeon General* (U.S. Department of Health and Human Services, Centers for Disease Control and Prevention, National Center for Chronic Disease Prevention and Health Promotion, Office on Smoking and Health, 2000).

reasons to seek help in trying to quit. The good thing about the similarities between nicotine dependency and other dependencies is that you have an opportunity to use a proven program, the Twelve Steps, that millions of others have used to successfully recover from other addictions.

Recovery from nicotine addiction can begin by combining an adaptation of the Twelve Steps with other tobacco-cessation resources including treatment programs. (Treatment program goals and approaches are outlined on pages 26–29.) The following pages suggest ways to apply each of the Twelve Steps to recovery from nicotine addiction.

STEP ONE
Who's Powerless? What Unmanageability?

We admitted we were powerless over nicotine—
that our lives had become unmanageable.

Admitting powerlessness over smoking means admitting we can't control our tobacco use. By accepting our nicotine addiction and all its consequences, we open the door to change— or at least we stick a toe in the door and prop it open a bit. In order to begin this exciting recovery process, the first order of business is to lay out the problem and look at our helplessness in the face of it.

Ask yourself a few questions:

- How often have I promised myself or others that I would quit smoking or using tobacco?
- How many times have I actually tried to quit and failed?
- How often have I tried to reduce my tobacco use without success?
- Have I continued to use tobacco even though it produced negative consequences in my life?

Here are some more questions to ask yourself about the unmanageability of a life that revolves around nicotine addiction:

- Have I ever avoided nonsmoking people, places, or situations?
- Have I ever avoided sports or other physical activities because I knew I'd get winded and probably wouldn't perform well?
- How much money have I spent each year on tobacco (money perhaps needed for other things)?
- Have I ever been late for appointments because I had to catch a smoke before getting there?
- Have I ever gone out at odd hours because I realized there wasn't a cigarette or other tobacco product in the house?
- Have I ever secured my supply, making sure I wouldn't run out unexpectedly?

And here are a few more questions: Can you make a phone call without lighting up? What happens when you face a tense situation such as an argument with your spouse or a confrontation with a co-worker? Can you start the day without a cigarette? Or finish a meal without one?

What unmanageability? The list is virtually endless. When we prepare the Fourth Step inventory later on, we'll see exactly how unmanageable our lives have become. For now, we need only admit that we're not able to control our tobacco use, and, as a result, we've done things and become people we may not like.

Step One requires some humility—it's hard to admit and accept that we aren't in control of nicotine, that nicotine controls us. Because consequences for tobacco use are not immediate but occur over a longer period of time, it can be easy to ignore or deny the fact that we aren't in control of this aspect of our lives. The notion of willpower, pervasive in our culture today, makes it even more difficult to say out loud, "I can't quit. I'm not in control of my tobacco use." But the admission—and the humility that comes with it—represents the first step toward making real changes in our lives.

STEP TWO
Believe and Imagine

*Came to believe that a Power greater than ourselves
could restore us to sanity.*

Step Two asks us to think about relating to someone or
something outside of ourselves. It asks only that we accept
these ideas:

- Something outside of ourselves is greater than we are.

- This greater force can help.

We're asked in this Step to do two things:

- Learn to believe and trust in something or someone outside
  ourselves.

- Imagine who or what that Power is.

To come to trust in a Power outside ourselves, we need to
acknowledge the insanity of our tobacco use. *Insanity* may
sound like too strong a word, but how else can we explain continued use of a substance that will injure or kill us in time? It
might be worthwhile to make a simple list. Go back over the
last few years, and write down the methods you (operating on
your own power) have used to control your tobacco use. Here
is a checklist:

- Have you given yourself an allotment of cigarettes or other
  tobacco to use per day?

- Have you switched to a brand you don't like?

- Have you bought low-tar tobacco products?

- Have you tapered down tobacco use to meet some alleged
  quitting date?

How often have you tried, relying on your own resources, to
reduce or stop smoking? When we honestly accept that we've

tried and failed more times than we can count, it becomes easier to understand and accept the insanity of our continued tobacco use and to look outside ourselves for help.

We then need to create a concept of a Higher Power and fix it in our minds and hearts. It must be a reality we can imagine, know, trust, and feel comfortable with. These questions might help you settle on a version of a Higher Power you can rely on to restore you to sanity:

- Do you remember having a strong spiritually or emotionally moving experience? What moved you? Can you translate that into a Higher Power?

- Does being a part of nature give you a sense of humility and of being in the presence of a Power beyond your understanding? Can you translate that feeling into a concept of a Higher Power?

- If your God is the one of your childhood, can you create a warm and supporting image of that God in your mind?

- Can you use the significant people in your life for a Higher Power or, at least, as a Power outside of yourself? Or can you use a group of people, such as a recovering smokers' support group or another Twelve Step group?

If accepting a Power greater than yourself is difficult, your Higher Power can be a good sponsor who has experienced long-term abstinence from tobacco.

The spiritual aspect of this Step helps strengthen the relationships in our lives, which in turn supports our efforts to change and grow and heal. The process of defining and accepting a Power greater than ourselves opens the door to cultivating a bond with others, with ourselves, and with a Higher Power. Healthy relationships in all of these areas lead to balanced living and diminish the need for our addictive relationship to nicotine.

STEP THREE
Outside Myself

*Made a decision to turn our will and our lives
over to the care of God,* as we understood Him.

Turning our will and our lives over means allowing positive
forces outside ourselves to help us. It means reaching out and
trusting that, when we turn over our addiction to nicotine, a
strong hand will be there to take it from us.

Telling others about our struggles helps a great deal.
Unfortunately, social acceptance of smoking and other tobacco
use often means that people around us don't interfere and are
unaware we're struggling with an addiction. We can hold the
secret in forever if we choose to. This would be using the same
denial and enabling syndrome that operates in alcoholism and
other drug dependencies.

Developing social support is one of the key aspects of
successful addiction treatment. Turning the problem over goes
hand in hand with reaching out to and developing a network
of people and help. Here are some sources of support:

- Family members

- Friends

- Co-workers

- Nicotine Anonymous or Smokers Anonymous groups

- Members of a smoking-cessation clinic, program, or group

- A sponsor, buddy, or support person paired with you through
  a smoking-cessation program

And, of course, your Higher Power is with you constantly,
offering a solution within every problem you confront—if
only you remain quiet enough inside to sense the gentle
nudges in the right direction.

Once again, the issue of willpower can block progress with Step Three. The Step begs us to answer one key question: who's in charge? If we believe in willpower, then the answer is, "we are." But if we can let go of the idea that we *should* be able to control our tobacco use, then willpower becomes a moot issue, one we can step over as we choose to turn the addiction over.

STEP FOUR

Reflections in the Mirror

Made a searching and fearless moral inventory of ourselves.

The Fourth Step inventory, one of the greatest sources of help within the Twelve Steps, allows us to see where we've been and where we want to go. Step Four involves making an honest and thorough moral inventory that includes both our strengths and our weaknesses. The inventory, though sometimes painful, unlocks many of the secrets that keep us prisoner and protect our addiction. If we do it honestly and thoroughly, we create a mirror in which we can see exactly who we are, to determine our future steps.

There are many ways of preparing a good Fourth Step. When making your inventory, use pen and paper and *write it down*. Begin by asking yourself the following five questions. Then, list examples under each one. The topics under each question are intended to help you think of specific examples.

1. **How does my smoking affect me?**
   Physical and medical problems?
   Self-image?
   Emotional balance?
   Vitality and energy?
   Preoccupation?
   Financially?
   Spiritually?

2. **How does my smoking affect others?**
   At home?
   At work?
   In social situations?
   Preoccupation?
   Financially?
   Role modeling for children?
   Safety at home, in the car?

3. **What situations trigger the need to smoke?**
   Phone calls or other specific activities?
   Boredom?
   Confrontation and anger?
   Anxious times?
   Emergencies?

4. **What character defects feed my addiction to nicotine?**
   Insecurities, fears, anxieties?
   Lack of positive self-image, confidence?
   Excessive pride?
   Controlling behavior?
   Impatience?
   Anger?

5. **What strengths do I have that I can draw on to quit and stay quit?**
   Persistence?
   Determination?
   Courage to change?
   Love for self and others?
   Problem-solving skills?
   Self-knowledge?

Be honest in thinking about how tobacco use affects you. Think about activities you avoided because you didn't have the energy. Think about preoccupation—how you felt when you discovered you were out of tobacco at eleven o'clock at night. Or perhaps you hoarded cigarettes by buying a carton for home, one for work, and one for the car just to make sure you wouldn't run out. Add up how much money you think you've spent every day of each year you've been smoking or using other forms of tobacco. And think about how you felt when you had to spend an evening with nonsmoking friends or sit through a daylong seminar in a nonsmoking environment.

Be equally honest about how your tobacco use—for example, just the smoke itself—has affected others. Beyond the obvious, think through the subtleties. What kind of role model have you presented for children and teenagers? Did you pass up any family or other social activities for lack of energy? Did you sit and watch TV instead of going swimming or biking with the kids or with friends or with your spouse, to avoid physical exertion? How has your physical condition affected your activity level and the kinds of friends you have? What about the health effects of secondary smoke on your children, spouse, and others?

Last, think through the habit itself. When do you use tobacco? Why do you use it at these particular times? What does it do for you? List the specific situations in one column and then list the character defects that feed the situation in the opposite column. For example:

Situation	Character Defect
Phone calls	Insecurity about my ability to control or please the person I'm talking to
Crisis	Fear of losing control, of not responding "correctly" to the situation

When you finish your list, you'll have a clearer reflection of where you stand with your addiction. But don't stop just yet. Pair up your character defects with your assets—you'll draw from this pool to change the behaviors you've listed above.

After searching within ourselves for solutions, the decision to turn it all over is pure relief. We're tired, beaten, and ready to take direction to grow again, to be alive.

STEP FIVE
Talking It Out

Admitted to God, to ourselves, and to another human being the exact nature of our wrongs.

Twelve Steps and Twelve Traditions introduces Step Five with these words:

> All of A.A.'s Twelve Steps ask us to go contrary to our natural desires . . . they all deflate our egos. When it comes to ego deflation, few Steps are harder to take than Five. But scarcely any Step is more necessary to longtime sobriety and peace of mind than this one.
>
> A.A. experience has taught us we cannot live alone with our pressing problems and the character defects which cause or aggravate them.[6]

In a nutshell, this is the essence of Step Five. It's the opening up in Step Five that allows a Power greater than ourselves to enter, stepping between us and our addiction. This opening up is also a powerful way of quelling the loneliness and sense of isolation—that feeling that we don't quite belong—that feed

---

6. *Twelve Steps and Twelve Traditions* (New York: AA World Services, Inc., 1952), 55. Reprinted with permission of AA World Services, Inc. (See editor's note on copyright page.)

our obsession with tobacco use. Nicotine medicates our fears, giving us the illusion of having something to fall back on in every possible situation.

Talking this through with another person creates an open door, through which other people and our Higher Power can enter and help. Talking it out also helps us correct any rationalizing or sidestepping we did in preparing the Fourth Step inventory. This spoken inventory reflects as honest a picture as we can achieve—and the truer the reflection, the stronger our recovery.

Talking your inventory through with an appropriate person is important. You'll need to trust that person and rely on his or her ability to listen without judging or advising. Here are some people you might choose:

- A friend or family member who is abstinent from tobacco use

- If you're a member, your Nicotine Anonymous or Smokers Anonymous group or someone in it you trust

- A clergyperson or spiritual leader you trust and who does not use tobacco

- If you're participating in one, your smoking-cessation program group—or a counselor or group leader

Think of Step Five as an opportunity to gain perspective on yourself, to develop a true picture of who you are by accurately seeing the strengths and weaknesses that are part of your unique personality. Not everyone has the chance to see himself or herself as others do. Not everyone is fortunate enough to experience an event in life that leads to the development of deep personal insight. Though the problem that causes your need for honest reflection may be difficult, you can choose to accept, even welcome, it as a way to living a richer, more conscious, and insightful life.

Perfection Is the Downfall

Were entirely ready to have God remove
all these defects of character.

Read that again. It says "entirely ready." We may as well let go of our perfectionism right now and admit that practically no one is entirely ready to give up an addiction. We realize the incredible power of our addiction to tobacco when we see that even though it is life threatening, we still would rather not give it up just yet.

But even if we can't claim to be entirely ready, we can try to be. And that's what Step Six is about. It's a process of readying ourselves. Honesty is essential. We must be honest in admitting that perhaps we aren't entirely ready to give up tobacco. We must also be honest about our willingness to have our character defects removed. If there are a few defects we're unwilling to give up, we must work at saying, "I'm not ready to give that up just yet" rather than saying, "I won't let go of this."

One exercise that might help you with Step Six uses the lists you made in Step Four. Remember the exercise of listing specific situations in one column and the associated character defects in another? Take the list out, look it over, and ask yourself some questions that will help you relate your nicotine addiction to character defects:

- Which defects are causing me the most trouble? Why?

- Am I ready to have those defects removed?

- What will I lose or gain with each defect if I choose to keep it?

- What will I lose or gain with each defect if I choose to turn it over?

- Can I replace each defect I'm willing to give up with something that nurtures me?

If we approach Step Six as though we're going to be perfect at achieving entire readiness, we won't succeed. Perfectionism will contribute to our downfall. All this Step requires is readiness. It asks us to work at being willing to give up our shortcomings.

In some ways Step Six can be difficult, because it means living life *without* tobacco and *with* someone else in the driver's seat. If we have truly turned our will and our lives over to a Power outside of ourselves, we have relinquished control. Giving up control and, at the same time, our relationship with the "friend" who was always there when needed can produce a great deal of anxiety. But remember, readiness is all this Step asks of us.

STEP SEVEN
Strength from Weakness

Humbly asked Him to remove our shortcomings.

As addicts, we've never been able to claim humility as one of our strong points. Self-sufficiency and self-centeredness are the two traits that block humility and feed our personal liabilities. Requesting help rather than demanding satisfaction is the difference between humility and selfish pride.

Let's go back to the first three Steps for a moment. First, we had to admit powerlessness over tobacco use. That requires humility. Then we came to believe in a Power greater than ourselves, and we made a decision to turn over our wills and our lives to a Higher Power. Humility is also necessary to take these giant Steps. Step Seven asks us to draw on that humility to help us overcome our other shortcomings—the problem attitudes and behaviors we identified in the Fourth Step inventory.

One key to successful treatment for drug dependency is learning new attitudes and behaviors to replace nicotine-driven ones. Step Seven helps us clear some space for new ways of thinking and acting. These exercises may help you with Step Seven:

- Review the lists you made in Step Four.

- Write down the shortcomings you're willing to give up.

- Ask your Higher Power, either in meditation or in writing, to take them over for you.

- Promise yourself and your Higher Power that you'll keep the list of your remaining defects in front of you, and keep working at turning them over!

Simply ending tobacco use doesn't guarantee recovery. We need to replace tobacco as the center of our lives. This means we must work on our shortcomings—asking our Higher Power to remove them—to make room for growth and change. We must learn other ways to meet our needs and replace our addiction with a new center of living. From our weakness we find strength.

STEP EIGHT
Joining Others

Made a list of all persons we had harmed, and became willing to make amends to them all.

It's far too easy to pretend that our tobacco use hasn't hurt anybody. And often, societal attitudes reinforce our denial by condoning tobacco use, ignoring it, or looking right past it—even though we're killing ourselves and exposing others to deadly toxins. But, if we've done our Fourth and Fifth Step work honestly and thoroughly, the list of those we've harmed will come to us with little difficulty.

Making a list of those we have harmed requires that we go beyond what we did in the Fourth Step inventory—and for good reason. It asks that we be specific about whom we have

18

hurt and in what ways. Though painful, this process rewards us greatly by helping us relate better to others.

Here are some suggestions for outlining the plan of action asked for in Steps Eight and Nine. Remember, though, as you do this, Step Eight asks only that you "become willing."

- Write out a list of people you think you harmed as a result of your nicotine addiction.

- Prioritize your list, putting first those to whom you feel it's most important to make amends.

- After each name, write out a brief description of the ways you feel your tobacco use has affected or harmed that person.

In preparing this list, we'll learn of the harm we've done to ourselves, we'll explore our relations with others, and we'll gain tremendous insight into ourselves and our problems— life-giving insights that encourage growth and change. For example, if we've allowed our addiction to isolate us from others, making this list is the beginning of taking down the barriers that caused the isolation.

We can't forget ourselves in this exercise. We've harmed ourselves as well as others, so apologies should also be directed to the person in the mirror. When we become willing to accept the negative attitudes and behavior and other ways in which our tobacco use may have caused harm, we clear the way to living more responsibly with ourselves and others.

STEP NINE
Reaching Out

Made direct amends to such people wherever possible,
except when to do so would injure them or others.

Consider the heart of Step Nine. It asks that we accept the consequences of our past attitudes and behavior and take responsibility for the well-being of ourselves and others.

These are healthy, positive goals to work toward, and the rewards are many.

We may be tempted to avoid making amends by denying that our tobacco use affected anyone other than ourselves. After all, it's our bodies that were affected, right? That's right, so we should add ourselves to the list of those to whom we should make amends. But tobacco use affected others as well, as the answers to these questions will show:

- Whom did I expose to secondary smoke when I used tobacco?

- Did I make and break any promises about slowing or stopping use? Were those to whom I made promises disappointed or disillusioned with me as a result of my failure to quit?

- Whom did I inconvenience by needing to use tobacco or find and secure it?

- Which young people were exposed to my role modeling the use of tobacco?

Only we can know to whom we should make amends, when we should do it, and how. Making amends doesn't have to be complicated or laborious—a simple, straightforward approach is all that's necessary.

We should do some preparation, however, to develop a positive attitude about making amends and an appropriate sense of timing. We must remember that our mission is to make amends—not to predict the outcome. That's in the hands of our Higher Power. Timing is also important, but again, if we're quiet enough inside, our Higher Power will nudge us when the time is right.

To accomplish Step Nine, you may want to do the following:

- Review the list you made in Step Eight, and then set it aside for several days.

- Take the list out and look it over again. Are there people on the list you find hard to face or make amends to, for some reason?

- Discuss these names with your sponsor or with a good friend. Try to discover the reason for your internal struggle. Then decide if it's still appropriate to make amends to these people.

- Don't procrastinate. If it seems appropriate, contact the people you want to make amends to and set up a definite time to meet and talk with them.

- Anticipate what you want to say and how. Role-play with a sponsor or friend, if necessary.

- Then go out and do it, but remember to turn the outcome over to your Higher Power.

Step Nine helps us by improving our relations with others and by helping us to feel at peace with ourselves.

STEP TEN
Maintaining Balance

Continued to take personal inventory, and when we were wrong, promptly admitted it.

Steps Ten, Eleven, and Twelve help us maintain the balance we need in order to remain abstinent from tobacco use.

Step Ten is a joyous Step, because through it we take the whole Twelve Step program and apply it daily. It asks us to continually survey our assets and defects, to accept what we find, and to change or correct what is wrong. This continual assessment helps us maintain the emotional balance necessary to remain abstinent from tobacco use. This balance helps us stay on course and provides the stability that allows a directed, purposeful journey. Without balance, our ability to remain free of our addiction to nicotine will be jeopardized repeatedly—perhaps often enough that we'll succumb and relapse.

Step Ten helps us to be right with ourselves and with others. It gives us the opportunity to check our attitudes and behavior throughout the day. In this way, it gives us a great opportunity to make the most of every minute of the day and rewards us with change and growth. What more can we ask?

Developing healthy behaviors and attitudes is important to recovery from dependence on drugs like nicotine. Ongoing abstinence from nicotine depends on maintaining the new attitudes and changed behaviors we have learned. Here is an early-warning-signal checklist you can use weekly or monthly to check up on yourself:

- Am I assertive in my dealings with others? Am I taking care of my needs?

- Am I staying away from places and people who challenge my ability to remain tobacco-free?

- Am I taking concrete steps to make new friends and find new environments that are healthier for me?

- Am I active? Have I increased my leisure activities and physical exercise?

- What concrete methods, other than tobacco use, have I found to deal with difficult or stressful situations?

- Have I stayed in touch with those in my support network? Do I contact them when I need help?

- Have I harmed anyone? Have I made amends to them?

Through Step Ten, we learn to stop, check, correct, and move on. As this skill develops, the pool of resources we have to draw on in hard times expands. And our ability to remain abstinent during good and bad times is strengthened. Thus, we find balance.

STEP ELEVEN
Feed Your Soul

Sought through prayer and meditation to improve our conscious contact with God as we understood Him, praying only for knowledge of His will for us and the power to carry that out.

Another important aspect of maintaining abstinence from tobacco involves feeding our souls. Spiritual balance is essential. And balance means cultivating a steady spiritual relationship or sense of spirituality. We're no longer praying hard only when a bad situation presents itself, and then promptly losing contact when the heat is off.

This Step calls for a sustaining, nurturing kind of contact with a Higher Power that requires cultivation and discipline. Initially, "acting as if" often helps us develop regular conscious contact.

And what does this conscious contact do for us? It uplifts our minds and hearts, takes us out of ourselves, and opens us to strengths that we simply don't have within ourselves alone. It reinforces our humility, gives us a kind of grace that levels life's bumps, and helps us keep our lives balanced. Asking for knowledge of the will of our Higher Power, and the strength to carry out that will, gives our feet movement and direction.

One thing you can do with Step Eleven is to concentrate on the meditation aspects of the Step. Meditation implies taking time out for yourself and using your mental energy and resources to alter your state of mind. This process is like a relaxation technique that calms you, helps you achieve or maintain a good attitude, and ultimately helps you feel better— all essential tools to avoid relapse to tobacco use. Try this:

- Set aside at least three regular times each day to meditate.

- Find a place to go during each meditation period where it's quiet and you won't be interrupted.

- At first, use the time to simply relax your body and keep your mind quiet.

- When you can do this easily, move on to using the meditation time for thought, prayer, or whatever best helps you maintain a state of peace during the moments of meditation.

- Learn to use these meditation skills in difficult or stressful situations—anytime you feel the urge to use tobacco.

By caring for our bodies, minds, and souls, we can give ourselves a vital element that we need to survive—air. And we assure ourselves of the ability to breathe it.

STEP TWELVE
Others Need Your Message

*Having had a spiritual awakening as the result of these
steps, we tried to carry this message to other nicotine users,
and to practice these principles in all our affairs.*

Awakening. Really working on these Steps awakens us. As though from a very deep sleep, our senses come alive because we've tapped a well of resources that deepens the significance of all our acts. We become aware of these resources by practicing each Step repeatedly. We're now ready to share with others what we've learned.

Many people need to hear our message. We probably each know at least ten people in trouble with tobacco use. We may have looked past their nicotine problem, just as others ignored ours. Offering help and support to others in need requires action and gives back rewards. When we offer a helping hand, we find out what we've learned and how we've grown.

Here are a few ways you can carry the message to others:

- Attend a Nicotine Anonymous or Smokers Anonymous group.

- When you feel you're ready, offer to be a sponsor for someone who's trying to quit using tobacco.

- If you've completed a smoking-cessation program, volunteer some of your time to help out.

- Offer encouragement to family members, friends, or co-workers who are trying to abstain from tobacco use.

Remember the maxim that says the more you give, the more you receive. This is the heart of Step Twelve. Our spiritual awakening gives us a sense of joy, of life. If we practice these principles in all our affairs, we can spread that joy around with no fear of diminishing our ever-renewing pool. We give it away in order to keep it.

Quitting Tips

You can take many steps to prepare yourself to successfully quit using nicotine. You may not need to use all of the following suggestions, but some combination of these steps can strengthen your efforts.

- Make a list of good reasons to quit using tobacco. Take it with you wherever you go and read it when you are tempted to use tobacco.

- With a physician, investigate the possibility of using a pharmacological intervention to help you abstain from tobacco. This may be in the form of nicotine chewing gum, nicotine transdermal patch, or medications. See the discussion on pages 27–28 for more information about each of these treatments.

- Look for a good smoking-cessation program to enroll in. Your physician can recommend a program or you can contact the organizations listed on pages 29–30 to find a program that fits your needs.

- Find out if there is a Nicotine Anonymous group in your area and begin attending meetings.

- Start working each Step of the Twelve Step program and develop a strong relationship with your Higher Power, whether that be a friend, sponsor, group, or whatever Power outside yourself that you envision.

- Find a sponsor, someone who has quit using tobacco and can offer you support when you need it.

- Avoid perfectionism in breaking the habit.

- Identify your tobacco-use patterns; choose one pattern a week and break it (put off that first cigarette in the morning; quit smoking in meetings, in the car, after meals, on the phone).

- Don't quit forever—just quit for one day at a time.

- If you relapse, quit again. Assess what led to the relapse and address those issues as you start working your recovery program once again.

- Tell your family, friends, and co-workers that you're quitting.

- Avoid rationalizing your way back to tobacco use by smoking "light" or low-tar cigarettes or by telling yourself that "just one" won't hurt.

- Make smoking each cigarette a decision—bring it to your conscious mind, rather than let it be the unthinking, repetitive behavior it has become.

- Pick a day to quit—and quit. It's time to enjoy life!

Treatment Approaches

Though some of us learn to abstain from tobacco use by ourselves, many of us need help to quit and to maintain abstinence. The surgeon general's 2000 report states that pharmacological treatment combined with behavioral programs yields the highest success rate both for initial quitting and for remaining abstinent for at least one year. Pharmacological treatments include various forms of nicotine replacement (such as gum, patch, sprays, inhalers) or medication.

The following summary of pharmacological and smoking-cessation programs will allow you to assess the kind of help you might need.

Pharmacological Treatments

Recent research indicates that those who quit using tobacco gradually using a pharmacological treatment, who have psychological support, and who learn skills to handle high-risk situations have the highest long-term rates of abstinence.

To recover from nicotine addiction, the first thing you must do is stop using the drug. To help you do this, you might consider using a treatment such as nicotine gum, a patch, a nasal spray, or an inhaler. By replacing nicotine, these treatments reduce the need to use your primary source of nicotine (cigarettes, chewing tobacco, etc.) as well as reduce drug-seeking, or nicotine-seeking, behavior. Though the urge to smoke or use other forms of tobacco won't disappear, withdrawal symptoms will be reduced or eliminated, allowing you to maintain normal social and work responsibilities while you quit using tobacco.

Pharmacological treatments include:

- *Nicotine chewing gum and nicotine transdermal patch* are available over-the-counter. They deliver enough nicotine to prevent withdrawal symptoms but not enough to give the stimulant effect that results from using tobacco.

- *Nicotine nasal sprays and inhalers* are available by prescription and also act as nicotine replacements.

- *Medications* such as Zyban don't replace nicotine but instead work on areas of the brain to help control cravings or thoughts about tobacco use. Zyban is the trademark name for bupropion, an antidepressant medication that is effective for some people in treating nicotine addiction. Zyban is available by prescription.

Smoking-Cessation Programs

Many smoking-cessation programs exist—how can you evaluate which one best fits your needs? First, keep in mind the two primary goals of treatment for nicotine addiction:

- *To stop smoking* or to eliminate use of the substance you are dependent on, whether it's cigarettes or other forms of tobacco.

- *To avoid relapse* or to maintain your abstinence from the use of nicotine.

The important thing to remember regarding the first goal— to stop using nicotine—is that setting a goal of merely reducing your intake isn't helpful; no level of cigarette smoking or ingestion of other tobacco products is safe. The second goal—avoiding relapse—is vital to recovery. Ongoing factors such as stress and exposure to people and places associated with nicotine use create continual invitations to relapse.

The best treatment approaches contain both physiological (smoking-cessation) and behavioral (maintenance of abstinence) components. These help you achieve an immediate goal of stopping tobacco use while giving you new skills to cope with ongoing behavioral and environmental pressures.

Treatment approaches that will help you make necessary behavior changes take many forms. Programs might combine individual, group, and family counseling with skills training and buddy support systems.

Because maintaining abstinence is such a major goal, it's important to find a treatment program that offers skills training in several areas. According to the surgeon general's report, people who have developed skills in the areas of relapse prevention, leisure activities, stress management, and social support are best able to maintain abstinence from nicotine.

- *Relapse prevention skills* include training in assertiveness, social skills, problem solving, and practice in handling high-risk situations.

- *Leisure skills* involve learning or relearning relaxation and recreation activities, particularly physical activities and exercise.

- *Stress management skills* involve learning to deal with negative emotions associated with difficult events or relationships.

- *Social support skills* involve finding support from friends, family, support groups, counselors, peers, or sponsors to help you maintain ongoing abstinence.

Where to Go for Help

It's hard to fight any addiction, and tobacco use is no different. But you can quit! More than forty million Americans have successfully quit smoking. Check the phone book white pages to find listings for Smokers Anonymous or Nicotine Anonymous and the yellow pages under Smoking or Drug Abuse for local smoking-cessation resources. You can also contact the human resources office where you work; many companies have information about employee smoking-cessation programs. A variety of organizations offer information on how to quit and where to go for help.

If you want to quit smoking and need help, talk with your health-care provider and seek out information, advice, and suggestions for beginning the end of your tobacco use. The following list represents some of the organizations that offer varying kinds of help for quitting tobacco use.

Agency for Healthcare Research and Quality
1-800-358-9295 for a "You Can Quit Smoking"
   consumer guide
www.ahcpr.gov

American Cancer Society
1-800-ACS-2345
www.cancer.org

For pregnant women:
American College of Obstetricians and Gynecologists
1-800-762-2264
www.acog.org

American Heart Association
1-800-242-8721
www.americanheart.org

American Lung Association
1-800-LUNG-USA
www.lungusa.org

Centers for Disease Control (CDC)
1-800-311-3435
www.cdc.gov/tobacco

National Cancer Institute
1-800-4-CANCER
www.nci.nih.gov

National Institute on Drug Abuse (NIDA)
1-888-644-6432
www.drugabuse.gov

National Women's Health Information Center (NWHIC)
1-800-994-WOMAN
www.4woman.gov

Nicotine Anonymous
415-750-0328
www.nicotine-anonymous.org

The Twelve Steps of Alcoholics Anonymous*

1. We admitted we were powerless over alcohol—that our lives had become unmanageable.

2. Came to believe that a Power greater than ourselves could restore us to sanity.

3. Made a decision to turn our will and our lives over to the care of God *as we understood Him.*

4. Made a searching and fearless moral inventory of ourselves.

5. Admitted to God, to ourselves, and to another human being the exact nature of our wrongs.

6. Were entirely ready to have God remove all these defects of character.

7. Humbly asked Him to remove our shortcomings.

8. Made a list of all persons we had harmed, and became willing to make amends to them all.

9. Made direct amends to such people wherever possible, except when to do so would injure them or others.

10. Continued to take personal inventory and when we were wrong promptly admitted it.

11. Sought through prayer and meditation to improve our conscious contact with God *as we understood Him,* praying only for knowledge of His will for us and the power to carry that out.

12. Having had a spiritual awakening as the result of these steps, we tried to carry this message to alcoholics, and to practice these principles in all our affairs.

* The Twelve Steps of AA are taken from *Alcoholics Anonymous,* 3d ed., published by AA World Services, Inc., New York, N.Y., 59–60. Reprinted with permission of AA World Services, Inc. (See editor's note on copyright page.)

Twelve Steps *for* Tobacco Users
FOR PEOPLE ADDICTED TO NICOTINE

Discover a way of changing attitudes and behavior in order to enjoy a lifestyle of long-term, tobacco-free living. Offering hope and help for those addicted to nicotine, this pamphlet adapts the Twelve Step philosophy—which has successfully helped people overcome dependencies to alcohol and other drugs—to tobacco and nicotine. This new edition includes updated information on nicotine's addictive nature, its effect on special populations, and its impact on young people's lives, along with online resources for help.

Other titles of interest . . .

Recovery from Smoking
Quitting with the
Twelve Step Process
Newly revised, second edition.
Softcover, 168 pp.
Order no. 5407

If Only I Could Quit
Recovering from Nicotine Addiction
Personal stories and meditations
by Karen Casey. Softcover, 320 pp.
Order no. 5031

The Nicotine Quit Kit
Workbooks, journal, video, audios,
goal card, relaxation card,
relapse warning signs card, and
rewards envelope.
Order no. 0271

Breathing Easy Collection
Positive strategies to manage nicotine
cravings. Set of four forty-page booklets.
Order no. 5979

Breathing Easy
A Journal for Living Nicotine-Free
A collection of ninety-six affirmations.
Journal, 102 pp.
Order no. 1132

Breathing Easy
Meditations on Living Nicotine-Free
Absorb these affirmations from the
journal while driving, resting, working,
or exercising. CD, 45 min.
Order no. 2748

$3.75+

HAZELDEN

15251 Pleasant Valley Road, P.O. Box 176
Center City, MN 55012-0176

1-800-328-9000 (U.S. and Canada)
1-651-213-4000 (Outside the U.S. and Canada)
1-651-213-4590 (Fax)
www.hazelden.org (Online)

ISBN 978-0-89486-229-8
90000

9 780894 862298

Order No. 1419